Snow White

and the Seven Dwarfs

Miles Kelly

One winter's day, a baby girl was born to a king and queen. She was very pretty, with skin as white as snow and lips as red as blood.
S
She was named Snow White before her mother sadly died.

The king remarried, but his new queen was unkind and vain. She had a magic mirror, to which she would say,
"Mirror, mirror, on the wall, who is the fairest of them all?"
"You, O queen are the fairest of them all!"

Many years later, when Snow White was sixteen, the queen asked this same question, and the mirror replied:
"You, O queen, are very fair – but Snow White is now the fairest."

The queen was absolutely furious!
She ordered a huntsman to find
her stepdaughter and kill her.

The huntsman took Snow White into the forest, but he could not bring himself to do the wicked deed.

Instead, he told Snow White to flee, and went back to the queen, pretending he had carried out her wishes.

"Run away, Snow White, and never come back!"

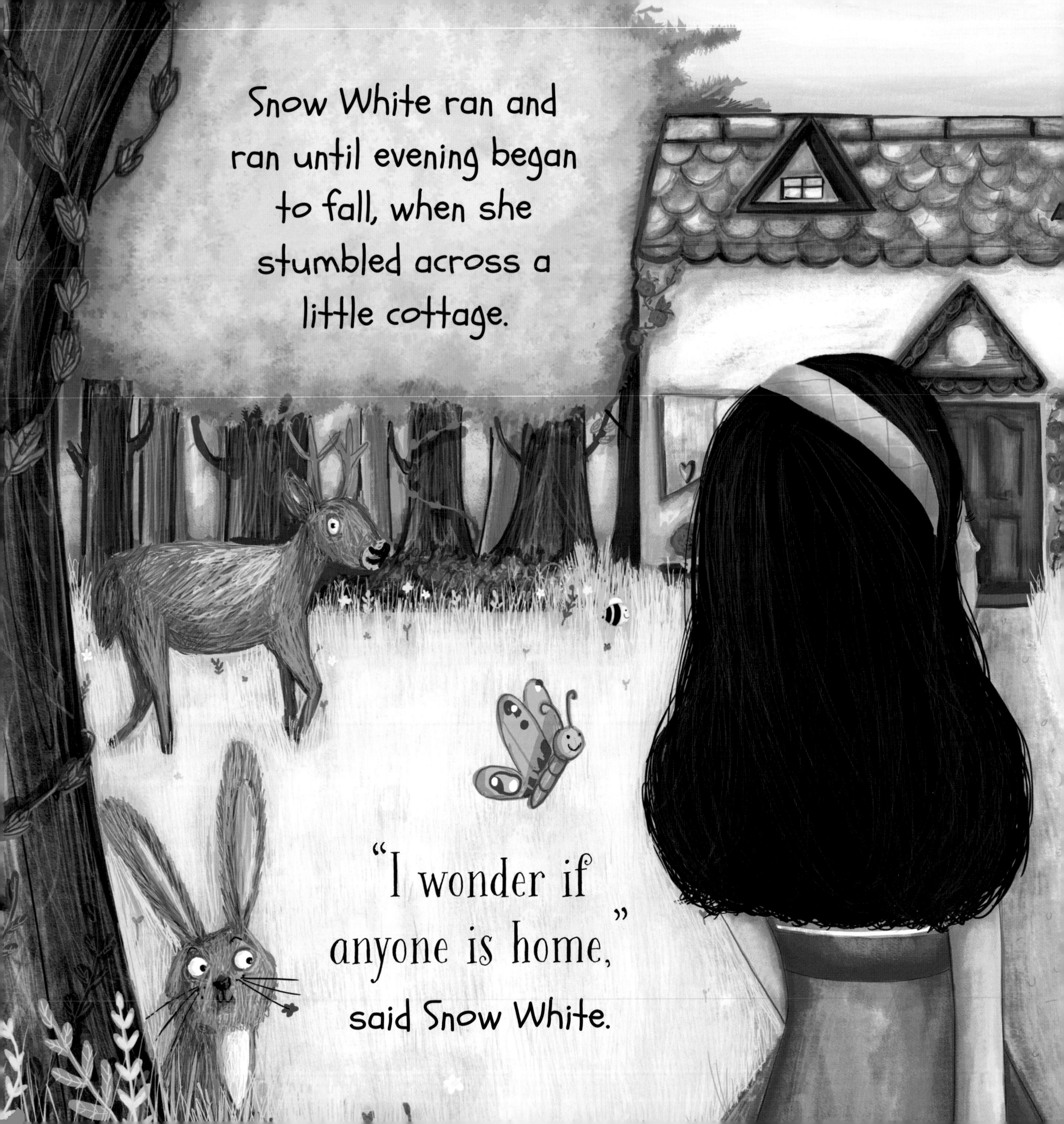

Snow White ran and ran until evening began to fall, when she stumbled across a little cottage.

"I wonder if anyone is home," said Snow White.

She walked up the path and
tried the door, and to Snow
White's surprise it opened.

She went inside the cottage to see if anyone was there. Everything inside was very

small and neat.

Against the wall stood seven little beds. Snow White sank down on one and soon fell fast asleep.

Later that night the owners of the cottage came back – they were seven dwarfs, who had been mining in the mountains for jewels.

When Snow White awoke she explained to the dwarfs what had happened. They kindly said,

"You are very welcome to stay here with us."

While the dwarfs went out to work Snow White looked after the cottage. Each day they warned her to beware of her stepmother.

But one day, months later, the magic mirror told the evil queen that Snow White was still alive!

"Snow White is in the forest!"

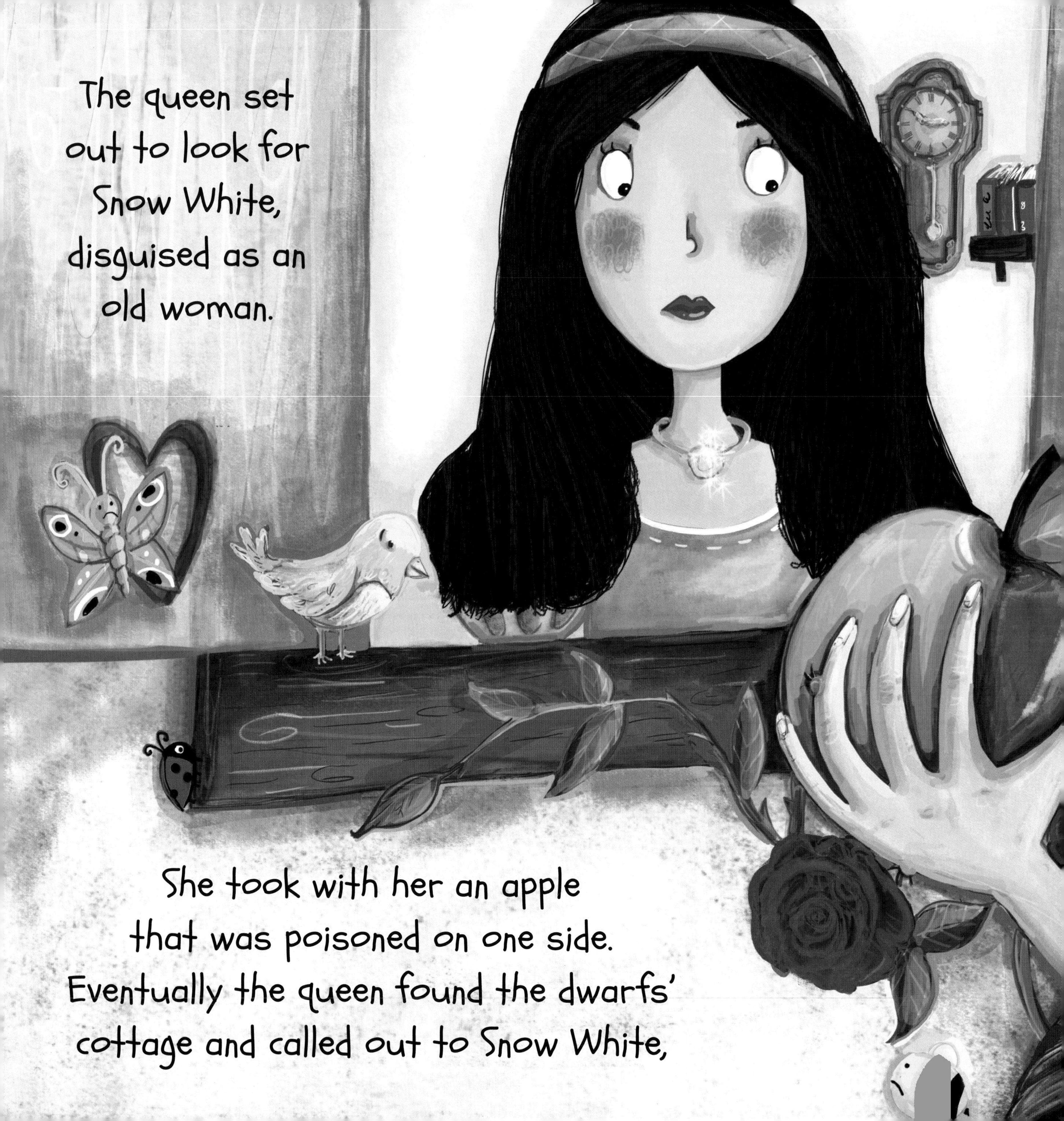

The queen set out to look for Snow White, disguised as an old woman.

She took with her an apple that was poisoned on one side. Eventually the queen found the dwarfs' cottage and called out to Snow White,

"Apples for sale!
Delicious, juicy,
sweet apples!"

"No, thank you" said Snow White, but the queen wouldn't take no for an answer.

She cut off a piece from the green half of the apple. "Look, I will eat some first. It is quite safe."

Snow White was hungry,
so she took the apple, taking a
bite from the rosy-red side.

Straight away
she fell down
as if dead!

When the dwarfs came home and found Snow White, they hugged each other and wept.

They made a glass coffin for Snow White. Very strangely, she always looked as if she had just fallen asleep.

One day a prince came riding past. He stopped to look at Snow White, but as he leant closer he knocked the coffin. The poisoned apple fell from her mouth and she awoke!

The prince took
Snow White to his
palace to recover, and
they soon fell in love.
The dwarfs were the
guests of honour
at the wedding!
Congratulations!

Meanwhile, the evil queen asked her mirror one last time, "Who is the fairest of them all?" And when she heard the answer – Snow White – she burst into flames!

And Snow White and the prince lived happily ever after.